THE FARMER IN THE DELL

A Singing Game

Pictures by
Mary Maki Rae

Scholastic Inc.
New York Toronto London Auckland Sydney

ISBN 0-590-42614-1

Copyright © 1988 by Mary Maki Rae.

All rights reserved. Published by Scholastic Inc.,
730 Broadway, New York, NY 10003, by arrangement with
Viking Penguin Inc.

12 11 10 9 8 7 6 5 4   1 2 3 4/9

Printed in the U.S.A.   08

First Scholastic printing, May 1989

*To all
buoyant,
light-hearted
children
of the future,
past,
and present*

The farmer in the dell,
The farmer in the dell,
Heigh-ho, the derry-o,
The farmer in the dell.

The farmer takes a wife,
The farmer takes a wife,
Heigh-ho, the derry-o,
The farmer takes a wife.

The wife takes a child,
The wife takes a child,
Heigh-ho, the derry-o,
The wife takes a child.

The child takes a nurse,
The child takes a nurse,
Heigh-ho, the derry-o,
The child takes a nurse.

The nurse takes a dog,
The nurse takes a dog,
Heigh-ho, the derry-o,
The nurse takes a dog.

The dog takes a cat,
The dog takes a cat,
Heigh-ho, the derry-o,
The dog takes a cat.

The cat takes a rat,
The cat takes a rat,
Heigh-ho, the derry-o,
The cat takes a rat.

The rat takes a cheese,
The rat takes a cheese,
Heigh-ho, the derry-o,
The rat takes a cheese.

The cheese stands alone!
The cheese stands alone!
Heigh-ho, the derry-o,
The cheese stands alone!

THE FARMER IN THE DELL

1. The farm - er in the dell,_____ The farm - er in the

dell,_____ Heigh - ho, the der - ry - o, The farm - er in the dell.____

2. The farmer takes a wife,
   The farmer takes a wife,
   Heigh-ho, the derry-o,
   The farmer takes a wife.

3. The wife takes a child, *etc.*

4. The child takes a nurse, *etc.*

5. The nurse takes a dog, *etc.*

6. The dog takes a cat, *etc.*

7. The cat takes a rat, *etc.*

8. The rat takes a cheese, *etc.*

9. The cheese stands alone! *etc.*

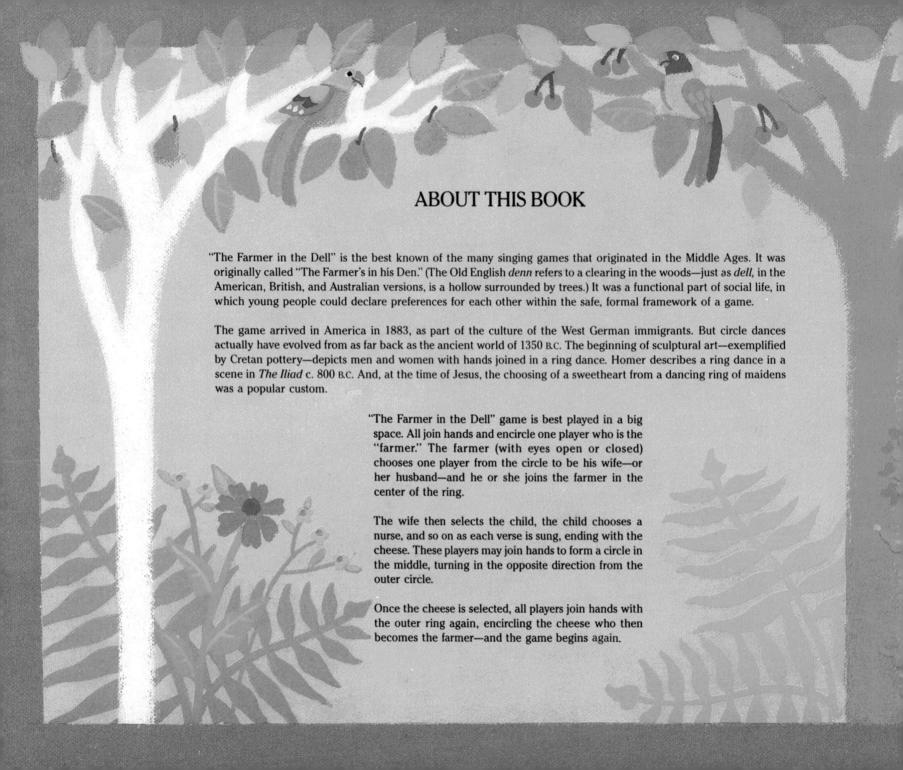

ABOUT THIS BOOK

"The Farmer in the Dell" is the best known of the many singing games that originated in the Middle Ages. It was originally called "The Farmer's in his Den." (The Old English *denn* refers to a clearing in the woods—just as *dell*, in the American, British, and Australian versions, is a hollow surrounded by trees.) It was a functional part of social life, in which young people could declare preferences for each other within the safe, formal framework of a game.

The game arrived in America in 1883, as part of the culture of the West German immigrants. But circle dances actually have evolved from as far back as the ancient world of 1350 B.C. The beginning of sculptural art—exemplified by Cretan pottery—depicts men and women with hands joined in a ring dance. Homer describes a ring dance in a scene in *The Iliad* c. 800 B.C. And, at the time of Jesus, the choosing of a sweetheart from a dancing ring of maidens was a popular custom.

"The Farmer in the Dell" game is best played in a big space. All join hands and encircle one player who is the "farmer." The farmer (with eyes open or closed) chooses one player from the circle to be his wife—or her husband—and he or she joins the farmer in the center of the ring.

The wife then selects the child, the child chooses a nurse, and so on as each verse is sung, ending with the cheese. These players may join hands to form a circle in the middle, turning in the opposite direction from the outer circle.

Once the cheese is selected, all players join hands with the outer ring again, encircling the cheese who then becomes the farmer—and the game begins again.

"The Farmer in the Dell" game is best played in a big space. All join hands and encircle one player who is the "farmer." The farmer (with eyes open or closed) chooses one player from the circle to be his wife—or her husband—and he or she joins the farmer in the center of the ring.

The wife then selects the child, the child chooses a nurse, and so on as each verse is sung, ending with the cheese. These players may join hands to form a circle in the middle, turning in the opposite direction from the outer circle.

Once the cheese is selected, all players join hands with the outer ring again, encircling the cheese who then becomes the farmer—and the game begins again.